VOCAL SELECTIONS from MACK & M...

MACK & MABEL

The Musical Romance of Mack Sennett's Funny and Fabulous Hollywood

DAVID MERRICK
presents

ROBERT **PRESTON**   BERNADETTE **PETERS**

in

MACK & MABEL

Book by
MICHAEL STEWART   *Music and Lyrics by*
JERRY HERMAN

Also Starring
LISA KIRK

with

JERRY DODGE	CHRISTOPHER MURNEY	TOM BATTEN
BERT MICHAELS	NANCY EVERS ROBERT FITCH	STANLEY SIMMONDS

and
JAMES MITCHELL

In Association with EDWIN H. MORRIS

Scenic Design by	*Costume Design by*	*Lighting Designed by*
ROBIN WAGNER	PATRICIA ZIPPRODT	THARON MUSSER

Musical Direction and Vocal Arrangement	*Orchestrations by*	*Dance Music by*
DONALD PIPPIN	PHILIP J. LANG	JOHN MORRIS

Associate Choreographer	*Production Supervisor*
BUDDY SCHWAB	LUCIA VICTOR

Associate Producer	*Based on an idea by*
JACK SCHLISSEL	LEONARD SPIGELGASS

Original Cast Album by ABC Records

Directed and Choreographed by
GOWER CHAMPION

© 2006 by Faber Music Ltd
First published by International Music Publications Ltd
International Music Publications Ltd is a Faber Music company
3 Queen Square, London WC1N 3AU
Printed in England by Caligraving Ltd
All rights reserved

ISBN10: 0-571-52836-8
EAN13: 978-0-571-52836-3

MACK & MABEL

Contents

Movies Were Movies

Music and Lyric by
JERRY HERMAN

1. Mov - ies were mov - ies when you paid a dime__ to es - cape,
2. Mov - ies were mov - ies when Pau - line was tied__ to the track
3. *(Instrumental)* - - - - - - - - - -

Cheer - ing the her - o and hiss - ing the man__ in the cape.
Af - ter she trudged__ through the ice with a babe__ on her back.

Ro - mance and ac - tion and thrills, Pard - ner, there's gold__ in them
Girls at the sea - shore would stand All in a row__ in the

Look What Happened To Mabel

Music and Lyric by
JERRY HERMAN

hold your snick - ers, for the new en - chant - ress of the flick - ers is that

plain lit - tle Nel - lie, the kid from the del - i, So rat - tle me beads,—

look what hap - pened to Ma - bel!—

D. S. al ⊕ Coda

⊕ *Coda*

ba - gels and knish - es, *Oh*
(Shouted)

Big Time

Music and Lyric by
JERRY HERMAN

Slowly and Freely

This time__ it's the big time;__ in a short time__ we can be

Moderate 4, (In Tempo)

The cher-ry on the top__ of the sun - dae,__ The shin - y star on top__ of the
This time we won't say, "Those luck-y bas - tards," This time those luck-y bas-tards are

tree. So you'd bet - ter grab it__ with your both hands__ when that
us. Ain't we some-thin'? Fare - well__ to the small time,__ to the

I Won't Send Roses

Music and Lyric by
JERRY HERMAN

Wherever He Ain't

Music and Lyric by
JERRY HERMAN

I Wanna Make The World Laugh

Music and Lyric by
JERRY HERMAN

Tap Your Troubles Away

Music and Lyric by
JERRY HERMAN

1. Tap ... your trou- bles a- way,
2. Tap ... your trou- bles a- way,
3. Tap ... your trou- bles a- way,

You've bounced— a big check, ... your mom— has the
You're sued— for di- vorce, ... your broth- er gets
A rag- ing ty- phoon, ... an earth- quake in

31

Hundreds Of Girls

Music and Lyric by
JERRY HERMAN

38

When Mabel Comes In The Room

Music and Lyric by
JERRY HERMAN

it's his way of say - ing, "Wel - come home, you've been gone too long."

The day you left us_____ was a small dis - as - ter;_____

_____ you took the love and light and laugh-ter and left the gloom._____

But I can feel my heart - beat_____ beat a lit - tle fast - er,_____

44

Time Heals Everything

Music and Lyric by
JERRY HERMAN

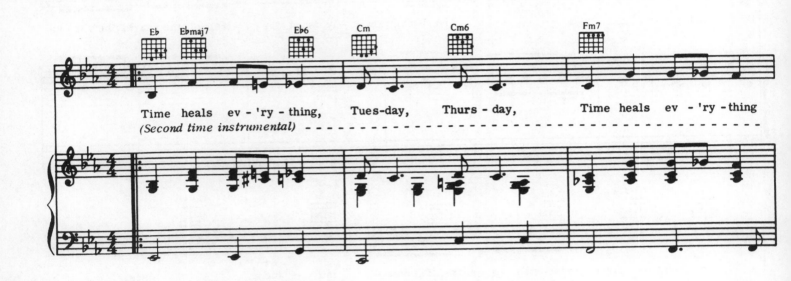

Time heals ev-'ry-thing, Tues-day, Thurs-day, Time heals ev-'ry-thing
(Second time instrumental) -

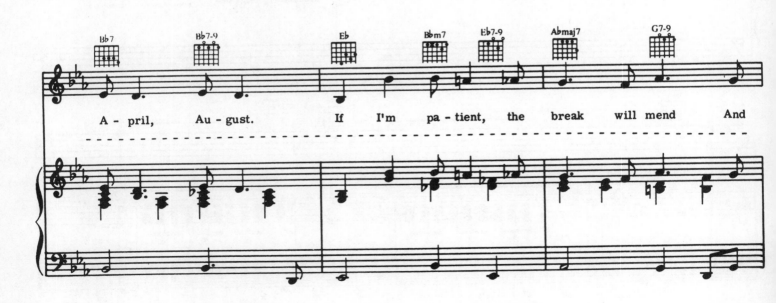

A-pril, Au-gust. If I'm pa-tient, the break will mend And

48

I Promise You A Happy Ending

Music and Lyric by
JERRY HERMAN

1. I pro - mise you a hap - py
pro - mise you a hap - py

end - ing Like the ones that you see on the screen. _____
end - ing Like the one you've been dream - ing a - bout. _____

Printed and bound in Great Britain 4/01